WHAT TO
EXPECT
WHEN YOUR HUMANS
ARE EXPECTING

Clifford Herriot

In the beginning,
you were the baby.

The center of attention.

The focal point of
every selfie.

They let you share their human food.

Your humans took you
to the park...

...and to the beach.

They bought
you toys

and silly
clothes.

Every day
was a
new
adventure.

But lately,
something
feels...
different.

When Mom gets in from work,
all she wants to
do is nap.

You may start thinking she needs to cut back on treats.

Walks include less walking and more stopping these days.

And
Mom's tummy
is now
HUGE!

She smells
like milk.

The cream she rubs on her belly tastes pretty good…

But there's not much room on her lap.

Whoa!
There's something
inside her tummy!

The humans
are waiting on
something.

But what
could it be?

One day, they come home with a bundle wrapped in a blanket.

It's a tiny human!

They might
even bring
home two.

Tiny humans smell kind of funny.

They taste funny, too.

And they'll have to housetrain it, just like a puppy.

Tiny humans cry.
A lot.

They take up way too much of Mom and Dad's time...

But soon,
you'll realize
that tiny humans
are kind of cute.

Especially once you learn how to make them laugh.

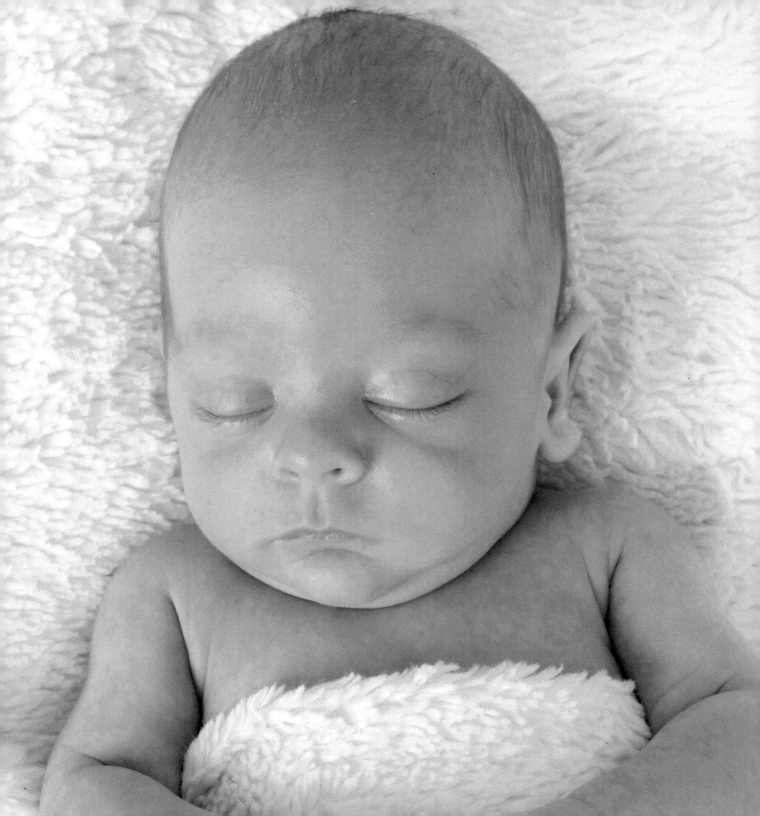

They'll share their food.

And expect to share yours.

Soon you'll be going to the park

...and to the beach again.

Keeping tiny humans safe
and happy isn't an easy job,
but if you're very patient
and give them lots of love…

You will have
a best friend
for life.

One big
happy
family.

Uh-oh.

A *bigger* happy family?

Here we go again!

This book is based on dozens of interviews with dogs who have welcomed tiny humans into their families. The author, Clifford Herriot, is not the Dog Whisperer, but dogs *do* whisper to him.

Published by Starry Night Books.

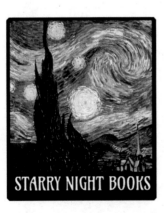

STARRY NIGHT BOOKS

PHOTO CREDITS
Cover: Erik Lam; Twenty20
Pages 1-2: Vadym Drobot
Pages 3-4: Daemaine; Tran Van Chieu; Arne Trautmann
Pages 5-6: Viacheslav Iakobchuk
Pages 7-8: Albert Shakirov
Pages 9-10: Simbiothy; Vadym Drobot
Pages 11-12: Liliya Kulianionak
Pages 13-14: NDAB Creativity
Pages 15-16: Iuliia Versta
Pages 17-18: Orsolya Szabo
Pages 19-20: Milan Ilic
Pages 21-22: Josep MªSuria
Pages 23-24: Vladimirs Poplavskis; Valengilda
Pages 25-26: Tatiana Dyuvbanova
Pages 27-28: Andrii Zorii
Pages 29-30: Yuliia Sonsedska
Pages 31-32: Tetiana Sokolova
Pages 33-34: David Herraez
Pages 35-36: Yurii Sokolov
Pages 37-38: Jacques Jacobsz; Tatyana Tomsickova
Pages 39-40: Patryk Kośmider
Pages 41-42: Petr Jilek; Olga Yastremska
Pages 43-44: Oksana Kuzmina
Pages 45-46: Leung Cho Pan; John McAllister
Pages 47-48: Johannes Kaufmann
Pages 49-50: Iciak Photos
Pages 51-52: Artranq Studios
Pages 53-54: Anurak Pongpatimet
Pages 55-56: Barbara Helgason
Pages 57-58: Twenty20 Photos; Martina Osmy
Pages 59-60: Evgeniy Kalinovskiy; Twenty20 Photos
Pages 61-62: Julia Strebkova
Pages 63-64: Andrew Lozovyi
Pages 65-66: Jaroslav Frank
Pages 67-68: Minko Peev
Back Cover: Cynoclub

Made in the USA
Monee, IL
05 January 2023

24595611R00043